# GEORGE WESTINGHOUSE

## 1846-1914

GEORGE WESTINGHOUSE, 1846-1914.

# GEORGE
# WESTINGHOUSE
# COMMEMORATION

A FORUM PRESENTING THE CAREER
AND ACHIEVEMENTS OF GEORGE WESTINGHOUSE
ON THE 90th ANNIVERSARY OF HIS BIRTH

CONDUCTED BY

## THE AMERICAN SOCIETY OF
## MECHANICAL ENGINEERS

December 1
1936

THE GEORGE WESTINGHOUSE MEMORIAL, SCHENLEY PARK, PITTSBURGH
The panels in the left and right wings depict the diversified achievements of his career.

# FOREWORD

The *Westinghouse Commemoration on December 1, 1936, sponsored by The American Society of Mechanical Engineers as a feature of its Annual Meeting, was originated two years earlier by the Council of the Society. The Council's action followed a report by C. N. Lauer, Past President, A.S.M.E., in which he said:*

The engineer is on the defensive in justifying his work and establishing himself as a constructive element in civilization and a driving force in providing for the well-being of mankind.

The American Society of Mechanical Engineers should dramatize the contributions of the outstanding leaders in engineering invention, design, construction, and application.

Such an opportunity occurs in 1936 in the celebration of the ninetieth birthday of George Westinghouse. As past president, honorary member, and John Fritz medalist, Mr. Westinghouse has helped to establish, and is representative of, the most treasured traditions of the A.S.M.E. It is fitting, therefore, that this Society should grasp the opportunity to make plain to the public the far-reaching results of the work of this great engineer on the occasion of the ninetieth anniversary of his birth.

*The committee in charge comprised Roy V. Wright, Past President, A.S.M.E., Editor of "The Railway Age," Chairman; S. W. Dudley, Dean of the School of Engineering of Yale University; James H. McGraw, McGraw-Hill Co.; Charles F. Scott, Professor of Electrical Engineering, Emeritus, Yale University; and the chairman of the Society's committee on meetings, R. I. Rees, succeeded by Ely C. Hutchinson. Later the Society invited the Westinghouse Air Brake Company and the Westinghouse Electric & Manufacturing Company to co-operate in*

CHARLES F. SCOTT

*arranging for a publication, and they appointed, respectively, John B. Wright, Assistant Vice-President, and W. G. Marshall, Vice-President, of their executive staffs.*

*The committee desired a more intimate and personal portrayal of the man than is usual in conventional biographies and a presentation of his achievements not only as things accomplished, but also in their historical perspective. It delegated Mr. Scott, who entered the Westinghouse Electric Company in 1888, to collect anecdotes and reminiscences and appraisals from associates of Westinghouse who could speak from personal knowledge. Selections from this material formed the basis of a unique presentation of the engineering achievements of Westinghouse. These were worked into a "continuity" in which nearly a score of those who knew his work—most of them long-time associates—told what he did and how he did it.*

*Following the afternoon presentation were evening addresses by a long-time and intimate associate, depicting The Man, and by a university president of wide outlook and keen discrimination, who traced the enduring results of his achievements.*

This edition is reprinted from the Society's publication, *Mechanical Engineering*, for March and April, 1937, by the Westinghouse Companies, with revised illustrations.

# THE PROGRAM

## *Afternoon Exercises*

ENGINEERING ACHIEVEMENTS
OF WESTINGHOUSE          *Page 9*
*A Panel Presentation by Associates and others*

## *Evening Addresses*

GEORGE WESTINGHOUSE, THE MAN      *Page 53*
PAUL D. CRAVATH, *Attorney, New York City*

ACHIEVEMENTS OF WESTINGHOUSE
AS FACTORS IN OUR MODERN LIFE      *Page 63*
JAMES ROWLAND ANGELL, *President of Yale University*

ON THE PLATFORM FOR THE WESTINGHOUSE FORUM
AFTERNOON EXERCISES

*Standing (left to right):* JOHN F. MILLER, N. W. STORER, THOMAS CAMPBELL, FRANCIS HODGKINSON, A. W. BERRESFORD, C. R. BEARDSLEY, ROY V. WRIGHT, CHARLES F. SCOTT. *Seated:* L. B. STILLWELL, W. W. NICHOLS, FRANK W. SMITH, E. R. HILL, J. V. B. DUER, SAMUEL M. VAUCLAIN.

# ENGINEERING ACHIEVEMENTS OF WESTINGHOUSE

## *Topics and Participants*

CHARLES F. SCOTT, *formerly with Westinghouse Electric & Manufacturing Company; since 1911, Yale University*—Leader

## WESTINGHOUSE IN PERSPECTIVE, *Introduction*

W. L. BATT, *President, A.S.M.E.*

## I. THE AIR BRAKE

RALPH BUDD, *President, Chicago, Burlington & Quincy Railroad*

W. W. NICHOLS, *Assistant to Chairman, Allis-Chalmers Manufacturing Company*

AMBROSE SWASEY, *Past President, A.S.M.E.*

THOMAS CAMPBELL, *Oldest Employee, Westinghouse Air Brake Company (Retired)*

## II. ALTERNATING CURRENT

A. W. BERRESFORD, *Past President, A.I.E.E.*

L. B. STILLWELL, *Consulting Electrical Engineer (Retired)*

C. R. BEARDSLEY, *Superintendent of Distribution, Brooklyn Edison Company*

## III. THE STEAM TURBINE

E. E. KELLER, *former Vice-President, Westinghouse Machine Company*

FRANCIS HODGKINSON, *Consulting Engineer, Westinghouse Electric & Manufacturing Company (Retired)*

FRANK W. SMITH, *President, Consolidated Edison Company*

## IV. RAILWAY ELECTRIFICATION

N. W. STORER, *Consulting Engineer, Westinghouse Electric & Manufacturing Company (Retired)*

S. M. VAUCLAIN, *Chairman, The Baldwin Locomotive Works*

GEORGE GIBBS, *Gibbs and Hill, Consulting Engineers*

W. S. MURRAY, *Consulting Engineer, formerly with New York, New Haven & Hartford Railroad*

J. V. B. DUER, *Chief Electrical Engineer, Pennsylvania Railroad*

## V. INDUSTRIAL RELATIONS

JOHN F. MILLER, *Vice-Chairman, Westinghouse Air Brake Company*

## EPILOGUE

CHARLES F. SCOTT

# WESTINGHOUSE IN PERSPECTIVE

Mr. Batt: We are gathered to celebrate the ninetieth anniversary of the birth of George Westinghouse by recounting his career and achievements. Westinghouse exemplifies the "rugged individualism" of the pioneers who built the America we inherit. He did not invade the wilds of the West but was a pioneer on the new social frontier where applied science and engineering and industry bend the forces of Nature to the practical welfare of the people.

Transportation and power—two great agencies in the industrial, economic, and social changes of recent times—were his chosen fields. To them he contributed new methods and mechanisms. He made the inventions of Watt and Stephenson and Faraday vastly more effective by extending their fields of operation and useful service.

Not merely an inventor or technical expert, he was an engineer in the broadest sense. To make Nature's elements of use to mankind involves the recognition of a need or an opportunity, the invention of some new method or device, and the development of the idea into concrete and practical form; then preparing for its production, convincing others of its usefulness, and supplying it for service. All these things Westinghouse did. He had facility in dealing with men and organizing them for research and development and manufacturing as well as facility in dealing with physical things, a rare combination of the complementary qualities of the two men who made the firm of Bolton and Watt successful in launching the steam engine.

Westinghouse was a self-made man. He had a grand inheritance—

physical, intellectual, moral. His liking for making new things was stabilized by routine work in his father's factory for manufacturing agricultural machinery. Hands and head worked together. The engineering of his day was empirical. He developed his own ideas of engines and mechanisms and made them himself before the days of schools with engineering laboratories. Air pressure and its control by valves became matters of intuition. He was alert, ingenious, capable, ambitious. In his advance from a boy working at the bench to the head of great industries, he acquired experience in every stage of industry, and he knew the workmen as his fellow-workers.

When he entered young manhood, the environment also was propitious as the stage was then set for a stirring act in the drama of transportation and power. The expansion following the Civil War created new demands with alluring opportunities; the railroads with 40 years of pioneering experience and century-old steam power, now giving new impetus to industry, were the beginnings on which to build.

To his heritage and environment he brought the dynamic power of a great personality. The last third of the nineteenth century was a period of phenomenal development in transportation and power and in industry as the little shop became the great corporation. And in those decades of engineering and industrial pioneering which made possible the enormous expansion that has been experienced since the turn of the century, Westinghouse was a leading actor.

He was acclaimed by his fellow engineers. The American Society of Mechanical Engineers made him its President and Honorary Member. The American Institute of Electrical Engineers awarded him the Edison Medal; the United Engineering Societies, the John Fritz Medal; the German engineers made him the first American recipient of the Grashof Medal. He had other medals and honors and degrees, American and foreign, but he was introduced to the International Railway Congress as its president in these words as "one who needs neither prefix nor affix to his name, George Westinghouse."

The evening addresses will deal with Westinghouse, The Man, and with the enduring influence of his career on human progress. This afternoon his engineering achievements will be reviewed by a group of men who are familiar with his work, many of whom were his associates. I ask Prof. C. F. Scott, who arranged this presentation, to act as the Leader. Professor Scott.

# I. THE AIR BRAKE

Mr. Scott (The Leader): In recounting the achievements of George Westinghouse we can tell of only a few of his activities; he had many others; his patents numbered nearly four hundred; and he organized 60 companies. Progress in science and engineering halts at times as some limit is reached. Then, perchance, a new discovery or invention brings release, and a new era develops. Thus, in the '60s, the Bessemer steel rail and a standard track gage and the joining of short roads into great systems portended a new era in transportation. But it was halted—safety at higher speed demanded an adequate brake. There was none. Progress awaited something new—it was a crisis. Fortunately we have Ralph Budd, president of the Burlington which figures in the Westinghouse story, who can tell us of the railroads and what they owe to Westinghouse. Mr. Budd.

Mr. Budd: This audience knows our dependence upon railroads. They have developed and unified America on a scale impossible by oxcarts and stagecoaches and canalboats. Industries rely upon railroads for transportation of raw materials and for distributing their products, while the public receives its winter's coal and its daily bread in freight cars.

The problem in the early days was to make locomotives powerful enough to pull trains; at first there were but few cars in each train. As they became longer and speeds greater, the problem was to stop the trains. Older men here today recall the whistle for "down brakes." Brakemen ran along the tops of freight cars, tightening brake wheels with pick handles as they passed from one car to another. They rushed through passenger coaches, turning the brake wheels on the open platforms, and, even then, the train often ran too far and had to back to the station.

Young Westinghouse saw the results of a collision that prompt braking would have prevented. He realized that the method of ap-

AIR DRILLING IN MONT CENIS TUNNEL, WHICH GAVE GEORGE
WESTINGHOUSE HIS INSPIRATION FOR THE AIR BRAKE.

plication was inadequate; brakes on all the cars should be operated
at once and by the engineer on the locomotive, but how? He considered buffer and chain-operated brakes and a steam pipe to cylinders
under each car, but found no good answer to his cumulative problem.
An attractive girl sold him a magazine; it told of compressed air driving rock drills in constructing Mont Cenis tunnel. In this he saw the
solution for his problem. Many difficulties were overcome, but, finally,
the Steubenville Accommodation out of Pittsburgh in April, 1869, a
year notable in railroad annals, had gone but a few hundred yards
when an emergency stop prevented a crossing accident and dramati-
cally acclaimed the merit of the air brake. Here was the result of three
years of effort, and it was the beginning of decades of development
to adapt the brake to longer trains and higher speeds. Without the
improved brake, high-speed trains as we know them, would be im-
practicable; indeed railroading as it is today would be impossible.
More than six hundred patents on brakes had been taken out when
Westinghouse entered the field; he climaxed them all, and the
principles which he developed have not been superseded.

Looking to the introduction of continuous brakes on freight trains,
the Burlington brake tests were held in 1886–1887. None of the five

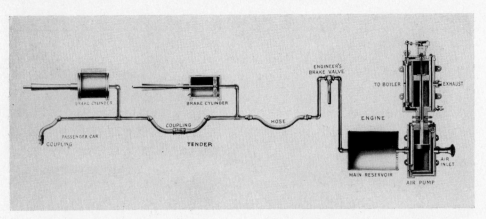

ORIGINAL WESTINGHOUSE AIR BRAKE, "STRAIGHT AIR" TYPE.

competing brakes was satisfactory to the railroads. The Westinghouse brake sufficed in service work but emergency applications produced shocks due to slow serial action. It was a crisis. A man who was there and had a part in the undertaking is here this afternoon. Let us ask him to tell the story. Mr. Nichols.

MR. NICHOLS: In the 1887 competitive air-brake tests, under the auspices of the Master Car Builders Association, following the defeat of Westinghouse by the Carpenter brake of Germany, "G. W." suddenly appeared on the scene to the relief of the distraught Westinghouse Air Brake Company officials whose agitation resolved itself into a sweet tranquillity. Indeed, one high executive observed to me, "Now that Mr. Westinghouse is here, everything will come right."

The trials had been at the West Burlington hill on the main line, and, as an engineer of tests, I had charge of the dynamometer car. Following the formal trials, Mr. Westinghouse instituted a private series of tests under M.C.B. conditions, and he spent much time during experimental runs studying the records and discussing, with me, their implications. Finally, one morning, he left impetuously before noon, inviting me to join him at lunch in his private car on the West Burlington Shops' siding. Later, as I passed through the corridor to the dining room, he emerged from his stateroom and waved a bit of

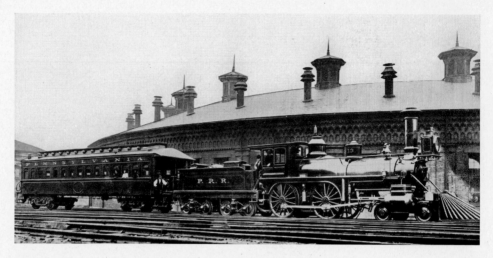

FIRST TRAIN EQUIPPED WITH AIR BRAKES FOR REGULAR SERVICE, 1869.

brown paper, exclaiming with characteristic enthusiasm, "Here's the triple that will revolutionize railroading!" How true that proved.

He hurried to the telegraph office and wired the factory preliminary specifications with orders to rush 50 triples, mailing his rude sketch to clarify his instructions. According to my recollection, the first test of the new triples proved a complete confirmation of his judgment, for the 50-car freight train, running on the level at 20 m.p.h., stopped in 98 ft., surprisingly without shock, both records without precedent. This contradicted the conclusions of the brake trials committee that "the best type of brake for freight service was one operated by air, *in which the valves were actuated by electricity*." But electricity, highly objectionable in such a service for many obvious reasons, he excluded in his new design, in whose application, as already remarked, "G. W." evidently visualized an amazing advance in train operation, since literally attained as every one knows.

Now, above all, the noteworthy event lay in "G. W.'s" returning home *before* a test of this triple; his sublime confidence in his inventive foresight made his presence at any trial utterly superfluous. As I wrote Colonel Prout, his biographer, a few years ago, "This was one of the most dramatic incidents of my career." No wonder the Colonel in his acknowledgment avowed that

It was so like "G. W." As long as I live, I shall regret that I did not understand G. W.'s soul while he was alive. I had to grow up to that understanding and that took quiet thought, and time was an element.

THE FAMOUS BURLINGTON TEST TRAIN OF 1887, EQUIPPED WITH
WESTINGHOUSE QUICK ACTION AUTOMATIC AIR BRAKES.

MR. BUDD: Mr. Nichols, we are indebted to you for this firsthand account of how a major improvement in the braking art was achieved. Now, I have the unique privilege of presenting a letter from a dear and long-time friend of George Westinghouse whom the Society also honors on this, his own ninetieth anniversary, our beloved Ambrose Swasey.

Cleveland, Ohio<br>Nov. 19, 1936

Dear Professor Scott:

I wish it were possible for me to speak at the Westinghouse Ninetieth Anniversary celebration, but it seems best that I should not attempt to do so.

On my return from a trip around the world in 1910, I said to Mr. Westinghouse:

When Mrs. Swasey and I were leaving Peking for Hankow, as we sat in the car, we heard the swish of the air under the car, and Mrs. Swasey asked what that meant. I said to her that the Chinese railroad men were testing the Westinghouse air brakes in order to see that they were in good condition before we started on our long journey across China.

And so, not only in China, but also in Japan, in Burma, in India, in Egypt, in Europe, and back to America, your air brakes were in use, and no one can estimate the prevention of destruction of equipment and the saving of life brought about by your wonderful invention, the air brake.

I certainly hope that some one will tell about the triple valve, that marvelous mechanism on which Mr. Westinghouse worked for many years. As our company

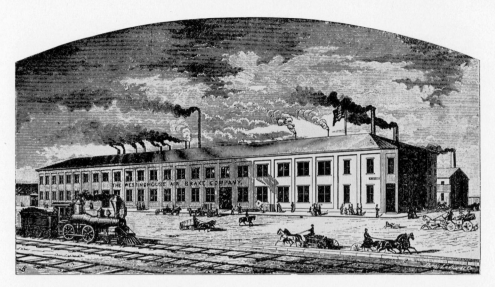

FIRST PLANT OF THE WESTINGHOUSE AIR BRAKE COMPANY
PITTSBURGH, PA., 1869.

made machines and tools for the manufacture of these valves, I was, of course, deeply interested in it. As the railroad was only 300 or 400 ft. from the old homestead where I lived as a boy, I remember so well the brakemen on the freight trains running from one car to the next to set the brakes as the trains went down a considerable grade in front of the house. This was counted as one of the most dangerous occupations in which men were engaged.

On going back to the old homestead in recent summers, I have taken particular notice of the trains of a hundred or more cars being stopped almost instantly by the same little triple valve. I am confident some one can tell a wonderful story regarding Mr. Westinghouse's genius in the development of this little mechanism.

With all good wishes, I am

Most sincerely yours,
AMBROSE SWASEY

Mr. Swasey's experience reminds me of seeing this same old friend from home, the Westinghouse air brake, on passenger trains in various parts of Russia. There, because the letter B takes the place of V and W, it is Bestinghouse, a modification that is complimentary to say the least.

Such is the story of a boy that a collision set to thinking; following the air brake, he developed air-operated railroad switches and automatic signals. Then came the friction draft gear for absorbing the blow of one car on another when starting and stopping, companion of the air brake in operating advancement; and later came railroad electrification. These are contributions of Westinghouse to safety, speed, and economy in transportation.

THE LEADER: One of the veterans of the Air Brake Company, Thomas Campbell, is here, and I want to ask him some questions regarding the early days. Mr. Campbell, what was the first thing you had to do with the air brake?

MR. CAMPBELL: The first equipment for the air brake was made by Atwood and McCaffrey, where I was learning my trade. I helped to make the first castings for the valves, and a few years later, in 1871, went to the 25th Street shop of the Air Brake Company.

THE LEADER: Why did you change?

MR. CAMPBELL: Why? Because at that time a man was considered lucky to get a job with the Westinghouse Company. Mr. Westinghouse inaugurated the piecework system and gave the men to understand through the superintendent, that the more money they made, the more the company made; $2.50 per day was good wages in other shops, while the men in the air-brake shops on piecework averaged $4.00 per day.

THE LEADER: What about shop equipment?

MR. CAMPBELL: Our shop had up-to-date tools; it had gear lathes, the first I ever saw; molding machines from Scotland were introduced in the foundry and were improved.

THE LEADER: How did he treat the men?

MR. CAMPBELL: He gave us each a dinner at the old Union Station Hotel. The men themselves have continued these dinners, and I have attended all of them. For many years he gave us each a turkey at Thanksgiving. He chartered a train and took us all to the Centennial at Philadelphia for a week in 1876. In 1881 the shops were moved to Allegheny, where washrooms and lockers were introduced so that we could come to the shop and leave in good clothes. He introduced the Saturday half holiday which we appreciated because there was a baseball field near by.

PRESENT PLANT OF THE WESTINGHOUSE AIR BRAKE COMPANY
WILMERDING, PA.

THE LEADER: Are you still working for the company?

MR. CAMPBELL: No. After more than 50 years of service, I retired. I am the oldest living Westinghouse employee. When they designed the Westinghouse Memorial in Schenley Park, I was the model to represent the mechanic; I hold a hammer and am proud of it. Since I retired, I have been receiving a monthly pension and am living comfortably with my son.

THE LEADER: Mr. Campbell, I think you told me that the Anderson boy, where Mr. Westinghouse boarded, used to invite you over as you were both musicians. What kind of music did Mr. Westinghouse like?

MR. CAMPBELL: He especially enjoyed the Scotch and Irish airs, the lively ones.

THE LEADER: Can't you give us a sample?

MR. CAMPBELL: I will be pleased to try.

[Mr. Campbell then took from his pocket a piccolo and played the Irish air, "Haste to the Wedding." As an encore he gave the Scotch air, "Money Musk."]

# II. ALTERNATING CURRENT

The Leader: And now we turn to electric power. Prof. Elihu Thomson told me that, at the Centennial in 1876, he was thrilled by a dynamo operating one arc lamp. Thus, the steam engine could now produce light as well as power and deliver it far beyond the reach of shafts and belts. A decade later there were commercial lamps and motors, but the distance by the prevalent Edison three-wire system was limited to a few thousand feet. Westinghouse, after establishing the air brake, took up railroad signals and natural gas, and established new industries. He investigated electric lighting. He secured Stanley and Shallenberger as experts and manufactured dynamos and lamps in a small way. He saw a great future if transmission distances could be extended. Then he read of transmission by high-voltage alternating current in Europe. The transformer seemed analogous to his reducing valve for high-pressure natural gas. He acted at once and made the year 1886 significant in the history of electric power. I introduce the chairman of the committee which commemorated the event, A. W. Berresford.

Mr. Berresford: The fiftieth anniversary of alternating current in America was celebrated on the twentieth of last March. Meetings of the American Institute of Electrical Engineers, which were conducted simultaneously in nearly 50 cities, recounted how Westinghouse brought the Gaulard and Gibbs system to America, how it was modified, and then given practical demonstration by Stanley at Great Barrington, and what has happened since.

But in Pittsburgh and Hartford, the March floods canceled the meetings; meeting places were waterlogged; power stations were submerged; electric service ceased. Night brought darkness. Nearly everything stopped: streetcars, elevators, newspaper presses, and electric pumps in city water works and in gasoline filling stations. Domestic appliances were inert: refrigerators, irons, doorbells, radios, clocks, and electrically controlled furnaces. Industries were at a standstill. Communication systems lost their operating current. It was tragic but, as only a major catastrophe can, it demonstrated the completeness of our present-day dependence on electric power as developed from the simple beginnings of a half-century ago.

THE LEADER: Just before the commercial installation of alternating current, L. B. Stillwell, a young college graduate, aided in preliminary tests. He became an important member of the technical staff in the eventful decade of engineering development that followed. Of this, he will tell us. Mr. Stillwell.

MR. STILLWELL: I have been invited to sketch in a very few minutes the work of George Westinghouse in the electric field in the decade preceding November, 1896, when polyphase alternating current from Niagara Falls was first delivered in Buffalo. In the time allotted, I can touch only some of the high spots of that progressive development which he directed with such masterful grasp and energy.

Mr. Westinghouse's great contribution to electric power lay in his early vision of its possibilities and his aggressive leadership in the development of alternating-current apparatus for realizing them. He was not an electrical expert. Nevertheless, in less than three weeks from the time he first saw a transformer, he made an outstanding contribution as an inventor. His mechanical design of the modern transformer is summarized by Reginald Belfield, who brought the Gaulard and Gibbs apparatus to America, in the following words:

Mr. Westinghouse applied himself toward the production of a piece of apparatus which could be wound on a lathe, utterly discarding the unpractical soldered joints and stamped copper disks for the more commercial form of ordinary insulated copper wire. It took Mr. Westinghouse only a few days to design an apparatus which has been the standard ever since.

GAULARD AND GIBBS
TRANSFORMER.

TRANSFORMER, WOUND ON A LATHE,
PATENTED BY WESTINGHOUSE, 1886.

This design was patented in 1886; it was soon followed by his patent on the oil-insulated transformer. It is a fact of peculiar interest to mechanical engineers that the problem of "turning the Gaulard transformer inside out" was solved with wonderful promptness by a great mechanician having, at that time, but little knowledge of the electrical factors involved.

The first commercial alternating-current plant at Buffalo began operation 50 years ago last Thursday. This was quickly followed by many similar plants in other cities.

Keen competition from the company manufacturing Edison apparatus, already in use, was at once encountered. Serious efforts were made in several states to secure legislation prohibiting line voltages exceeding 800 volts. Westinghouse opposed this move with his usual energy, and it did not succeed.

For Westinghouse and his staff at Pittsburgh, the technical problems were many. There was no alternating-current meter, no motor, and no arc lamp. Larger and more reliable generators, larger transformers, improved switches, lightning arresters, and incandescent lamps were needed. Stanley, at Great Barrington, and Shallenberger, Schmid, Belfield, and Lang, at Pittsburgh, worked with utmost energy,

FIRST COMMERCIAL ALTER-
NATOR, BUFFALO, 1886.

and the technical staff was increased gradually by employing young college graduates. Of these, seven have served since that time as President of the American Institute of Electrical Engineers. Mr. Byllesby once told me that when Westinghouse authorized him to increase the staff, he said: "There is but one rule that I must insist upon. I want you to employ none but gentlemen."

Westinghouse spent much time in the shop and laboratory of the Electric Company. A new device challenged his lively interest. His mental grasp was quick and definite, and his suggestions, even on purely electrical problems, were to the point and often fruitful. His attitude was encouraging and highly stimulating. Rarely did he lose patience even when his ideas were strongly opposed. When he occasionally expressed himself more emphatically than necessary, it was his habit, within a day or two, to make sure that cordial relations had been restored. While his temperament was masterful, he was habitually courteous.

In 1888 came Shallenberger's brilliant invention of the induction meter. In the same year Nikola Tesla was granted his United States patents covering the polyphase motor and system. Westinghouse promptly secured the American rights. Tesla came to Pittsburgh to develop his motor. He made vain attempts to adapt it to the existing single-phase, 133-cycle circuits. The polyphase power system and the obvious advantages of direct connection of engines and generators called for a lower frequency. In 1890 the company's engineers made a careful study to determine the frequency most suitable. Two frequencies were selected as standard, namely, 60 cycles for general use and 30 cycles for conversion into direct current.

In 1890, E. D. Adams, president of the Cataract Construction Company, and his chief engineer, Dr. Coleman Sellers, were in London. By invitation, Mr. Belfield and I discussed with them the problem of utilizing the power of Niagara Falls. Mr. Adams organized a com-

750 KW. ALTERNATING-CURRENT GENERATOR THAT SUPPLIED
ELECTRICITY FOR THE CHICAGO WORLD'S FAIR, 1893.

petition for the best solution of the problem. Cash prizes were offered. Anticipating the success of the Tesla motor, I urged the American Westinghouse Electric Company to submit plans. Mr. Westinghouse disapproved and later explained: "These people are trying to secure $100,000 worth of information for $3000. When they are ready to do business, we will submit our plans." The competition produced plans for transmitting power by compressed air and other nonelectrical means, also several electrical projects, nearly all for direct current.

Niagara presented an extraordinary opportunity to launch the polyphase system. It all seems obvious now, but, at that time, even Lord Kelvin, president of the Niagara Commission, which Mr. Adams organized, strongly opposed alternating current. The great need was a convincing demonstration. Westinghouse provided it. His bold adventure at the Chicago World's Fair in 1893 is a well-known story; apparatus not yet designed was essential; a patent injunction against the use of the "all-glass-globe" incandescent lamp was met by the stopper lamp. The result was a convincing demonstration of the polyphase system. As the Fair closed, a contract was executed for three two-phase alternators of "5000 electrical horsepower." The plant began operation in 1895, and, in November, 1896, Niagara power was transmitted to Buffalo. Lord Kelvin approved. A decade of electrical pioneering and development, beginning with the little single-phase lighting plant of 1886, ended with the polyphase plant at Niagara for supplying universal service. It laid the foundation in engineering system and in commercial confidence for the electric power expansion that has followed. Westinghouse's vision of an electric power system was realized.

THE LEADER: Returning from the works one evening, Mr. Westinghouse beckoned me to his seat and asked, "Do you know what they are going to do in Brooklyn?" I said that I did. "What do you think of it?" As substations were to supply the direct-current circuits from the alternating system which the recent development of a converter had made possible, I said that I thought it was a fine scheme. I was astounded when in a tone of keen disappointment he replied, "I am very sorry to hear you say so." Then, he added, "It should all be

GEORGE WESTINGHOUSE AND LORD KELVIN.

alternating." I had regarded the established three-wire direct current in cities as permanent. The sequel will be told by C. R. Beardsley, an engineer with the Brooklyn Edison Company. Mr. Beardsley.

MR. BEARDSLEY: The invitation to participate in this commemorative meeting honoring Mr. Westinghouse is very much appreciated. The establishment of a unified alternating-current distribution system is another fulfillment of his keen vision. The Brooklyn Edison Company began about 15 years ago to replace its direct-current, low-voltage distribution by alternating current. Direct-current substation capacity for a coincident peak load of about 80,000 kw. and the corresponding circuits were to be discarded and replaced by an alternating-current network. The network, in turn, was to be extended outward to displace the alternating-current radial feeds as the density of load warranted the change.

In addition to this large capital expense for network, there was the problem of changing consumers' services, meters, and utilization equipment, that is, direct-current motors and a large variety of direct-current devices which do not operate on alternating current. Some 130,000 consumers were served on direct-current circuits. The problems of surveying these premises, making new wiring layouts, and specifying the alternating-current equipment, and then satisfying consumers and obtaining permission to make the change were of huge proportions.

The change-over is virtually complete with approximately 225 consumers now being served on direct-current lines. These are, however,

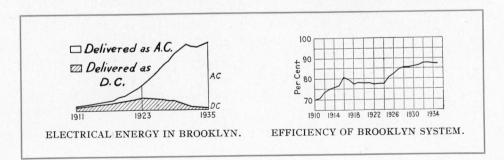

ELECTRICAL ENERGY IN BROOKLYN.   EFFICIENCY OF BROOKLYN SYSTEM.

some of the very large installations and most expensive to change. Completion is now in sight. As a result of this very considerable accomplishment, we have found that the prediction of advantages was well founded. Two thirds of the distribution losses have been saved; highly reliable service with better voltage regulation is obtained; additional capacity can be readily provided with the minimum of street operations, involving tearing up and repaving.

Thus, Brooklyn has been a large-scale pioneer in the shift to alternating current, first by interposing rotary-converter substations and now by doing away with direct current altogether. Nearly all the large cities are displacing direct-current service as the economic conditions warrant. Philadelphia has virtually completed the program. Detroit is making progress. Chicago is starting. Brooklyn was, however, one of the first to reach virtual completion and is thoroughly satisfied with the results. Thus, actual accomplishment proves the farsighted wisdom of Mr. Westinghouse's vision, to which Mr. Scott referred.

FIRST ALTERNATING-CURRENT GENERATORS INSTALLED AT
NIAGARA FALLS, 1895.

# III. THE STEAM TURBINE

THE LEADER: Electric power made new demands upon the steam engine. The old-time engine drove the machinery of a single mill; but an electric power station can send power to many mills and elsewhere.

Westinghouse became interested in making a new kind of engine long before there were any dynamos to be driven. By good fortune, his experiments prepared him to meet the new demands of electric power later on. E. E. Keller, Westinghouse manager at the Chicago World's Fair in 1893, became vice-president of the Westinghouse Machine Company that built steam and gas engines. He is unable to be present but sends a contribution which tells how Westinghouse acquired the turbine.

MR. KELLER: The old steam engine driving the machinery in his father's shop awakened the interest of young George Westinghouse. But why have a reciprocating engine to turn a shaft? He made a rotary engine and his first patent was for it and was issued before he was twenty. The rotary engine continued to be his hobby, and, in the '80s, he visioned an engine of high speed to avoid belts and to develop lower-cost electric generators. He redoubled his efforts, but, while his experimental rotaries awakened alluring hopes, they persisted in taking too much steam.

In 1895 he learned of a rotary engine working on the turbine principle. Its construction was unknown to us and became a subject for dinner-table discussion. A letter of inquiry brought a prompt response from Parsons. Westinghouse handed it to me, saying, "I wish you would go over to England and find out whether we ought to have this and if so, get it." On my asking his idea of its value, he replied, "I have not thought about price. I leave it entirely to your judgment. Only don't let it get away from us if it has merit. It is all up to you now. When can you sail?"

This conversation of maybe 20 minutes was an example of his direct, brief, and unique method of getting the best out of his associates and helpers.

I found that the turbine had not made much headway in general favor or in commercial application, but it seemed full of possibilities and promise, so I secured it. None of us fully realized then that this agreement was the death knell not only of Westinghouse's own rotary hobby, but also of the large reciprocating steam engine. It was an outstanding example of Westinghouse's farsighted vision of future needs and his indomitable courage in pioneering in new fields.

I not only secured the turbine, but, with greater difficulty, also acquired an engineer. Both have had a profound influence upon the development of power. The engineer is here and will now tell the story of the turbine. Mr. Francis Hodgkinson.

MR. HODGKINSON: Mr. Keller stated that the Parsons steam turbine had not been generally accepted in England when, in 1895, the interest of Mr. Westinghouse was aroused. Parsons began his activity in 1884, and it would seem that if his turbine had merit, it should have established itself within 11 years. Difficulties, not of an engineering character, however, had arisen; his partners had not the vision to go beyond the market for small electric generating sets principally for shipboard use. A dissolution of partnership ensued, in which Parsons lost the rights under his original patents, regaining them only a year before Mr. Keller appeared. Mr. Westinghouse's interest was excited by his vision of the possibilities of the steam turbine rather than by the success achieved on the part of Parsons.

The turbine of 1895 was confronted by many problems of technical detail, but a greater obstacle was the prevalent skepticism toward this high-speed innovation that depended upon jets of steam being directed, windmill fashion, against buckets, instead of expanding behind a comparatively leakless piston. This skepticism required the vision, courage, perseverance, and diplomacy of a George Westinghouse to overcome. He at once proceeded with the building of experimental machines, and, in 1898, he successfully undertook to demon-

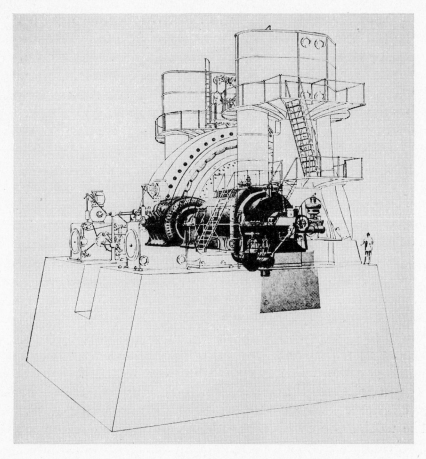

COMPARISON OF RECIPROCATING AND ROTARY TYPES OF
PRIME MOVERS.

strate their sufficiency and reliability by making the plant of the
Westinghouse Air Brake Company dependent upon them. The small
steam engines that were distributed throughout the factory for driving line shafting were discarded and replaced by electric motors.
Wires were substituted for steam pipes. The new power station was
equipped with three 300-kw. Westinghouse-Parsons turbine generators.
Mr. Westinghouse had spent some 30 years in endeavoring to develop a successful form of rotary engine. The turbine made his dreams
come true.

One year later, Mr. Westinghouse undertook the construction of a
1500-kw., 1200-r.p.m. unit, introducing some radical features of design, notably shortening the machine by tucking bearings, glands, and

other parts within the turbine rotor. Mr. Dunham heard of it before completion; he visited the works and purchased it for the Hartford Electric Light Company, of which he was president. Mr. Dunham was famous for courage in installing novel apparatus. This turbine had more than three times the capacity of any predecessor, and its construction, in the state of the art at that time, was a serious undertaking. It showed a high efficiency but not great reliability. Nevertheless, it made history, and, it is believed, gave the promise of success that led other manufacturers to enter the steam-turbine field.

This new prime mover came into competition with the reciprocating engine, then at the pinnacle of its development. Eight 5000-kw. engine-driven sets were being installed in the 40,000-kw. power station of the Manhattan Railway Company at New York, one of the largest of its day. These gigantic generators stood 42 ft. high and the low-pressure cylinders at each end of the shaft towered still higher. But, in less than 15 years, some of the reciprocators were replaced by three 30,000-kw. turbines, giving more than double the output of the eight huge engines. Later, more engines were replaced by a 70,-000-kw. turbine. It was indeed heart-rending to see these monarchs of engineering achievement being cut into bits with acetylene torches, for they represented the culmination of a century and a half of steam-engine history.

The turbine presented many advantages over the reciprocator. It was of less size, cost, and weight. It required less fuel, lubricating oil, and attendance. It could be built for vastly greater output. Other related instances of foresight on the part of Mr. Westinghouse were his espousal of the LeBlanc-condenser inventions, when his staff could see no virtue in them, and of the reduction gear by which a high-speed turbine could drive a slow-speed ship's propeller, thus rendering the advantages of the turbine available to ships of all kinds.

He was a great general, always inciting his staff to experiment and test. Frequently, he dominated details of design. He was an innate mechanician, but his knowledge of thermodynamics seemed limited, for he was sometimes led to ill-proportioning of the steam path and disappointment. Such occasions often led to unfortunate differences of opinion. I know that, frequently, he regarded me as quite an unfit person to design steam turbines. It was he, however, who introduced an advantageous combination of impulse-and-reaction-turbine elements and the single-double-flow principle.

EIGHT 5000 KW. STEAM-ENGINE-DRIVEN GENERATORS IN THE POWER
PLANT OF THE MANHATTAN RAILWAY COMPANY.

Withal, he was ever just and considerate, he was the most persua-
sive salesman I ever knew, be it in a discussion with a possible pur-
chaser or the sale of an idea to a subordinate. Never would he know-
ingly tolerate an injustice to an employee. He always had sympathy
for anyone in trouble, be it a bereavement, sickness, or what not. I
vividly remember one occasion; a large and important newly installed
machine got into trouble and was temporarily inoperative. It was a
serious situation for the company. On the day the news of the accident was received, I was on my way to lunch and saw George Westinghouse approaching. I became panic-stricken but could not dodge.
I expected to be party to a painful act of "I told you so." Instead,
there were *no* reproaches, nothing but kindliness and sympathy. His
sympathetic attitude caused my emotions to get the better of me.
Instead of going to lunch, I returned to my office to hide and weep.

THE LEADER: Mr. Hodgkinson has shown why the turbine is suited
to produce electric power for a city like New York. The company that
supplies most of this power has, as its president, a man who began
his career as an office boy in a power company, of which Mr. Westinghouse became the head. I now request the president of the Consolidated Edison Company of New York to tell us about the turbine
in the power stations of New York. Mr. Frank W. Smith.

MR. SMITH: I consider it a great personal privilege to be asked to pay tribute before this distinguished audience to the memory of George Westinghouse on this, the ninetieth anniversary of his birthday. It is true that I began work with one of our predecessor companies, the United States Illuminating Company, afterward the United Electric Light and Power Company, some 57 years ago. The latter company was the pioneer in producing and developing the alternating-current system in New York City. The United States Illuminating Company introduced the Weston series-arc lighting system and later, the limited series-multiple incandescent lighting system. The United Electric Light and Power Company was the pioneer in the introduction of the network system and was the first to apply the network system in its later development in an extensive way. With the perfection of this alternating-current network system in substitution for the old radial system, alternating-current distribution has become the standard of the world.

As a youthful employee, I saw Mr. Westinghouse from time to time, but, of course, in those early days, my contact was infrequent and more or less impersonal. In later years, however, my contact was

FIRST STEAM TURBINE, 120 KW., BUILT BY GEORGE WESTINGHOUSE 1896.

FIRST COMMERCIAL APPLICATION OF THE STEAM-TURBINE-DRIVEN
GENERATOR, 1500 KW. UNIT, IN POWER PLANT OF HARTFORD
ELECTRIC LIGHT CO., 1900.

more direct. I can well remember with what awe and esteem I regarded him. As the development of the alternating-current system
proceeded, the operation of this system with an overhead distribution
in competition, at that time, with the underground direct-current
Edison system was an exciting adventure. Our first power was produced by 130-kw. belted-engine generators, followed by 750-kw. steeple
compound-engine sets which were purchased by our company from
the Chicago World's Fair.

I can well remember being in our East 29th Street Station, now the
site of the enlarged Bellevue Hospital, with Mr. Westinghouse and
Caleb Jackson, an early president of the United Company, at the
time these units were installed. On the occasion of one of these visits,
the cylinder head of one of the units blew up and went through the
roof, returning by the natural force of gravity and disappearing
through the boiler-plate floor of the engine room. While this was not
a daily occurrence with these units, it was not infrequent, but they
were good engines for those days and did the job satisfactorily. If I
can remember correctly, when the accident occurred, I beat Messrs.
Westinghouse and Jackson to the street by five laps.

About 1900 the Edison Company laid out a great station of sixteen
3500-kw. generators, driven by Westinghouse engines. These units
were considered by many engineers to be so large that the company
could never find load for them. About the same time, the Manhattan

POWER SUPPLY OF NEW YORK CITY
*Requirements—2,000,000 Kw.*
Comparison of Engines vs. Turbines

| | ENGINES | TURBINES |
|---|---|---|
| Capacity Each (Kilowatts)................. | 7,500 (*largest ever built*) | 160,000 |
| Number Required........................ | 267 | 13 |
| Floor Area (Acres)....................... | 17.0 | 1.2 |
| Men Required to Oil...................... | 2,000 | 65 |
| Coal Required per Day (Tons)............. | 26,000 | 10,000 |

Saving per Year
In Cost of Oiler's Labor............. $ 5,000,000
In Cost of Coal..................... $30,000,000

Elevated Railway was being electrified with power supplied by 7500-kw. engine sets. These units were the largest of their type ever built and are about as large as it would be practical to build today.

The steam turbine was invented by Hero of Alexandria, before the Christian era; others, in the last decades of the nineteenth century, built turbogenerators which, however, neither in size nor efficiency, challenged the supremacy of the reciprocating engine, and the world had to wait 2000 years for the genius of George Westinghouse to visualize that the offspring of a union between the plaything of Hero and the alternating-current generator would become the universal burden bearer of mankind. As the prophet Joel foretold, many of our young men have seen visions and many of our old men have dreamed dreams, but to few, throughout the ages, has been given the practical idealism to make so many great dreams come true.

The present power requirements in greater New York are approximately 2,000,000 kw. To produce this power by the monster steam-engine outfits of 35 years ago, even with their increased rating, would require 267 units. The same output can be delivered by 13 steam turbines of the size now in operation, namely, 160,000 kw. The difference in coal consumption by the two types of unit amounts to 16,000 tons per day, which would load a freight train of 320 cars. The annual saving in coal is about $30,000,000. Thus, the practical idealism of Westinghouse is justified. His rotary type of prime mover, the subject of his first patent, joined with the alternating current, for the development of which he fought so vigorously, constitute our present power unit. The modern power station attests the soundness of his ideals and on a scale probably exceeding his own wildest dreams. This is one of the great romances in the career of George Westinghouse.

# IV. RAILWAY ELECTRIFICATION

THE LEADER: The railroad had an alluring interest for Westinghouse. As salesman for his car replacer and reversible steel frog, he met railroad men and learned their problems. Then came the air brake, and, later, his switch and signal system and the friction draft gear. But none of these supplied the power that moves the train.

Then he exploited electric power, entering the street-railway field with a superior motor in 1890. One of his electric-railway engineers recently retired after 45 years of service. N. W. Storer had to do with the development of all types of motor and made notable contributions to electric traction. He will tell the story of Westinghouse and railway electrification. Mr. Storer.

MR. STORER: The very first time I entered the Garrison Alley factory in the fall of 1891, it was my privilege to see George Westinghouse in action. He wanted to eliminate trolley wires from the streets and to collect current for cars from contacts or "buttons" projecting slightly above the pavement between the rails. He wanted to find what voltage would be safe on the exposed contacts. A short track had been arranged and a horse was ready. He was knocked flat by 110 volts; lower voltages were nearly as bad, and even 10 volts excited him greatly. The test stands out in my memory for two reasons. First, I saw Mr. Westinghouse in action, an experience that thrilled me and filled me with enthusiasm for the *man* and the *work* that I have never lost; and second, I have always felt that although direct current was used in that test, Mr. Westinghouse had in mind, even then, the use of single-phase alternating current with low voltage on the contacts.

FIRST SINGLE-PHASE CAR, 1894.

At any rate, B. G. Lamme not long after that produced a 25-hp. series motor for 3⅓-cycle current. Two of them were installed on a streetcar in 1894, and tested on an experimental track with a modified "button" system, near the Westinghouse residence. L. M. Aspinwall, who tested the equipment, recalled the "terrific" vibration at starting, due to the extremely low frequency, but the car was operated for several weeks. The low frequency was not satisfactory, but Mr. Westinghouse would not give up, and eventually Lamme developed a 100-hp. motor for 16⅔ cycles, five times the original frequency. Its announcement in 1902 started every manufacturer of electric-railway equipment developing single-phase motors. Mr. Westinghouse had taken a general interest in direct-current equipment and had worked with three-phase motors, but his ideal was a single-phase alternating-current system with high-voltage trolley and low-voltage series motors.

In 1904 the Grand Trunk Railway was considering the electrification of the St. Clair Tunnel. Quick action was necessary, and Mr. Westinghouse decided to build a single-phase locomotive for 25-cycle current to meet the requirements. Before it was completed, he invited the International Railway Congress, meeting in Washington, to come to East Pittsburgh to witness a demonstration of this locomotive and his friction draft gear which had just been developed. They accepted. A train of 50 steel gondolas, equipped with the friction draft gear, was tested first. It was hauled by one of the largest Penn-

EARLY SINGLE-PHASE LOCOMOTIVE.

sylvania freight locomotives. It handled the train well, but slipped its wheels repeatedly in accelerating. After a successful demonstration of the draft gear, the steam locomotive withdrew, and the electric took its place. The work of equipping the locomotive had been completed only the night before, so late that no preliminary tests had been made. But to our great relief and joy and to the amazement of the large crowd, containing many of the foremost railroad engineers in the world, the electric locomotive handled the train easily and quietly. The test was a complete success.

SINGLE-PHASE LOCOMOTIVE USED IN THE DEMONSTRATION FOR THE INTERNATIONAL RAILWAY CONGRESS, 1905.

The demonstration on that day in May, 1905, led to the adoption of single-phase electrification for the St. Clair Tunnel and also for the New York, New Haven & Hartford Railroad. Incidentally, it may be noted that the St. Clair Tunnel locomotive, after more than 20 years of service, was adopted with practically no change by the Pennsylvania Railroad as its standard electric locomotive for switching service. Thus the single-phase system was launched.

THE LEADER: In taking up, next, the commercial phase of railway electrification I planned to mention the Baldwin-Westinghouse arrangement and to introduce George Gibbs by saying that he had been recommended to Mr. Westinghouse by S. M. Vauclain, of The Baldwin Locomotive Works. But Mr. Vauclain is here, and I have the unexpected pleasure of asking him to speak. Mr. Vauclain.

MR. VAUCLAIN: It is not necessary, Mr. Chairman, for me to stand before the microphone as I think my voice will reach any person in such manner that he will understand what I have to say. My acquaintance with Mr. Westinghouse dates back to the year 1870. I say "Mr. Westinghouse" because George Westinghouse was always Mr. Westinghouse to me, and I never addressed him in any other manner. I well remember the first application of the Westinghouse air brake on the Pennsylvania Railroad; straight air, the old three-way cock with a brass plug by which the brake could be handled very successfully once you became acquainted with it. Occasionally, the passengers would be shaken up a little, but that was to be expected.

Later on, in the year 1890, when I was erecting some new buildings at The Baldwin Locomotive Works in Philadelphia, I had a serious talk with Mr. Westinghouse about driving all of our machinery and traveling cranes by electric motors. He remarked that I was taking a pretty big bite. However, notwithstanding his observations, it was decided that we electrify all the machinery and cranes in the building then being constructed, among which were two 100-ton cranes. The great difficulty in their construction was to find motors of sufficient capacity to drive them. The Westinghouse Company had taken over the United States Electric Company; therefore, I went over to see the people in charge, and they advised me that, if I didn't mind the weight, they could convert their lighting machines into motors. I agreed to this, and the order was placed. Those cranes were built and delivered and have been in operation 24 hours a day since the year 1890 and are at present in operation at the plant of The Baldwin Locomotive Works at Eddystone.

In the year 1895 The Baldwin Locomotive Works decided to build electric locomotives, and, in company with one of my partners, I went to Pittsburgh and proposed to Mr. Westinghouse that our two companies join in the enterprise. He promptly agreed to this. It was decided, after due discussion of the project, to secure an expert to be paid jointly by the two concerns. D. L. Barnes, an eminent engineer whose offices were in Chicago, was chosen. Fortunately or unfortunately, Mr. Barnes did not remain with the company very long. He had the idea that something startling had to be designed for electric locomotives, so as to attract attention, something similar to the attention now being given to streamlining of locomotives, cars, and so forth. It so happened that Mr. Barnes and one of our associates went duck shooting, as a result of which he became very ill and died. Our associate recovered after several weeks' illness.

Mr. Westinghouse called to see me immediately after Mr. Barnes' death, and said, "Vauclain, what are we going to do, now that Barnes is dead? We have no man, where will we get one?" "Well, that's all right," I said. "I can recommend you the best man in the country, George Gibbs," who was then mechanical engineer of the Chicago, Milwaukee & St. Paul Railroad Company, and now a consulting electrical engineer, of the firm of Gibbs & Hill, in this city. I explained to Mr. Westinghouse that Mr. Gibbs was associated with his brother and with J. N. Barr, then superintendent of motive power of the Milwaukee road, and was operating a small electric-motor-building plant in Milwaukee, and, inasmuch as I had found it difficult to get small electric motors for our machinery, I had given Mr. Gibbs many orders which he had filled to my entire satisfaction. I suggested that, in order to get him, it would be well for Mr. Westinghouse to buy out the Gibbs company and commence manufacturing small motors at the plant of the Westinghouse Electric & Manufacturing Company, and, at the same time, turn George Gibbs over to his company and hire him as our consulting engineer on electric locomotives and electrification of railroads. To suggest anything to Mr. Westinghouse

NEW HAVEN PASSENGER TRAIN ON HELL GATE BRIDGE.

that had any real value in it insured prompt action, and, in a very short time, he had bought out the Gibbs Electric Company, of Milwaukee, and George Gibbs became our mutual representative.

It may be well to note here that Mr. Westinghouse was always very much opposed to the third rail for transmitting power, and, today, after more than 40 years' experience, the third rail is seldom installed, although some installations are still in use.

The agreement then entered into, between Baldwin and Westinghouse, in 1895, still holds good, with only minor changes, and Baldwin-Westinghouse locomotives are found in all the principal countries of the world.

THE LEADER: My memory seems a bit slow this afternoon. In 1887 I began my electrical career as wireman at The Baldwin Locomotive Works. One day I was under a table in the drafting room fastening the wires to the table. I heard a great voice and I came out at once. Had I recalled that incident a few minutes ago, Mr. Vauclain, I would not have suggested that you needed a microphone.

Mr. Vauclain has told us about George Gibbs. As he is unable to be with us today, the other member of Gibbs & Hill will present his contribution. E. R. Hill was testing electric locomotives at East Pittsburgh some 40 years ago. Mr. Hill.

MR. GIBBS: Practical electric traction dates from 1887, when Frank Sprague's Richmond, Virginia, street railway began operation with 500-volt direct-current motors. This system was satisfactory for streetcars, but was unsuited for long distances or heavy service. As nothing else was available, progress in standard railroad electrification was slow. In the late '90s, alternating current began to be transmitted to substations, where it was converted through rotaries and supplied to the motors. Westinghouse and his engineers contributed to this system. But Westinghouse foresaw that the complete solution called for the flexible and economical distribution of current at high voltage to the locomotive. He advocated alternating current and urged that a common standard might have a future importance comparable to a standard track gage.

The utilization of the current on the locomotive was a second problem. He patented, in 1889, a scheme for converting, on the locomotive, the alternating current into direct current for driving the motors. It is, of course, desirable to avoid apparatus for conversion. The three-phase system uses alternating-current motors, and, although Westinghouse was developing this type of apparatus for general power and although it was used for railways in Europe, yet he held to his ideal of a single trolley and a simple alternating-current series motor for developing the power. It appears that he began work on this system quite early, and, refusing to compromise, he held to his ideal. As Mr. Storer has pointed out, success came a decade later. When the new system was announced in 1902, it was immediately adopted by a number of interurban lines, for which no other economical system was then available. But Mr. Westinghouse's real goal was heavy railroad electrification. Immediately following the demonstration of the single-phase locomotive before the International Railway Congress, of which he was president, he showed his confidence and his courage by proposing the new system on one of our most important railroad arteries, the main line of the New Haven Railroad between New

NEW HAVEN GEARLESS MOTOR.

MODERN SINGLE-PHASE LOCOMOTIVE.

York and New England. This important event will be described by the electrical engineer in charge of installation and early operation, Mr. Murray, who sends, by telegraph, his regrets and his contribution, which will be read by Roy V. Wright.

MR. MURRAY: As consulting engineer for the New Haven System, in association with E. H. McHenry, beginning 1905, it was our privilege to work out, with the Westinghouse Company, the details of the first heavy-traction, single-phase railroad electrification, but, behind us all, was the ever-guiding, dynamic, and indomitable spirit of George Westinghouse. He saw and sympathized with us in the seemingly insuperable difficulties of the application of a new engineering and construction art, but his great mind, holding principle above all else, never failed, nor did ours with his behind us. The New Haven electrification, first branded as a colossal failure, took the measure of the direct-current, third-rail system, eliminating its future use forever.

MR. GIBBS: The New Haven experience demonstrated possibilities in reduction of equipment costs and in giving hauling capacity for the heaviest requirements. It was followed by the important installations of the Norfolk & Western and the Virginian Railways and has culminated in the far-reaching installations of the Pennsylvania Railroad. This company had long experience in electric traction with direct current and with the single-phase system for its suburban service out of Philadelphia. The final outcome was the adoption of the single-phase system as used on the New Haven Railroad. I call upon the chief electrical engineer of the Pennsylvania Railroad. Mr. Duer.

MR. DUER: Single-phase electrification, adopted as standard on the Pennsylvania Railroad in 1915, after long experience with the direct-current, third-rail system which preceded it, has been developed and expanded until it is now used to operate the freight and passenger service between New York, Philadelphia, and Washington, one of the densest railroad traffics in the world. The conception of this system sprang from the genius of George Westinghouse and its development from the efforts of many engineers working resourcefully and intelligently to produce a system fully suitable for important railroad operation. Through the farsighted wisdom of the Westinghouse and General Electric Companies in co-operating in a joint development of locomotive and car equipments, these efforts have recently culminated in the most modern and successful types of power equipment in use on our railroad, and it gives me great pleasure to acknowledge our debt to George Westinghouse and express our profound appreciation for this great contribution to railroading.

MR. GIBBS: Some 50 years ago, back in the '80s, when Westinghouse was evolving a new triple valve, developing an automatic signal system, testing the friction draft gear, investigating the alternating-current transformer, and "playing" with his rotary engine, seemingly scattering his efforts over many unrelated fields, no one dreamed, unless it was Westinghouse himself, that they would some day all converge in a single project and produce the premier railway electrification of the world.

# V. INDUSTRIAL RELATIONS

THE LEADER: The air brake inaugurated a dual development; one a mechanism, the other an organization to make it. Westinghouse's acute understanding of the true principles underlying both mechanical operations and human relations enabled him to produce results which have endured. John F. Miller, associate of Westinghouse, long a directing force in the air-brake organization, now vice-chairman of its board, will tell of Westinghouse and industrial relations. Mr. Miller.

MR. MILLER: It is a notable fact that the Westinghouse Air Brake Company, organized in 1869, has never experienced a general strike. This can be attributed to the attitude of its founder toward his employees. As a worker in his father's shop at Schenectady, he naturally inherited the old-time conception of an employer as the head of a family of workmen who was responsible, in a way, for their welfare. In developing his air brake, he spent much time in the shop; a skilled mechanic himself, he often showed the workmen how to do what he wanted done. He knew them; they knew him; there was mutual understanding and esteem, genuine and lasting. And he had an enthusiasm that was contagious; others were ready to do their utmost for him. And, when numbers exceeded the range of his personal touch, those close to him were animated by his spirit and passed it on to others.

Mr. Westinghouse once said to a group of employees:

I want you to know and feel that no one has your best interests at heart more than I have. We are all interested in the same object, to make this company a success. I have my part in the job and you have yours and, if we all work together in friendly co-operation and with a feeling of mutual good will and good-fellowship, the desired result can never be in doubt.

The genuineness of his motives was attested by his acts. Some of these have been recalled by Mr. Campbell, one of the earliest of his "fellow-workers," as he often called them. The veteran has told us of the working conditions in the shop, of the trip to the Centennial, of the Thanksgiving turkeys. And did you note how he unconsciously referred to George Westinghouse, not as if he were a big boss, but as to a friendly father?

Increasing numbers led to difficulties in giving turkeys, and Mr. Westinghouse, though loath to give up the personal expression of good-fellowship, was induced to devote the turkey fund of $10,000 to the Westinghouse Air Brake Pension Fund. That early adventure into "social security," now the subject of so much discussion and new legislation, I cannot now describe in detail. It, however, developed into the broadest and most liberal provision for the "social security" of employees, of which I know. The fund now approximates $2,700,-000; the total benefits paid have exceeded $3,000,000.

The removal of the air-brake plant, in 1890, to a location 15 miles from the city was a new sort of industrial venture. It involved not only the building of a factory, but also the planning of a new town, including water supply, modern power system, and erection of dwellings. In all of these problems Mr. Westinghouse took keen personal interest, especially in those affecting the health, comfort, and well-being of his workmen. As a result, Wilmerding secured one of the earliest up-to-date sanitary sewer systems. Baths and toilet facilities were installed in the dwellings, which were far better than the average small dwelling house in the Pittsburgh district. Through a monthly payment plan, including life insurance, many employees became owners of their homes.

Social, educational, and recreational facilities were provided and substantially supported by the company. The Wilmerding Christian Association, the agency conducting the enterprise, now has a paying membership of more than 3300 men, women, and children. The town itself, a hamlet of a few houses in 1889, now has a population of 6300 and a taxable valuation of over $7,000,000.

In paying tribute to his attitude I cannot refrain from mention of his brother, Herman Westinghouse, member of The American Society of Mechanical Engineers, a leader in the Air Brake Company for nearly 50 years, until his death in 1933. In employee relations, he also was a shining example of the Westinghouse spirit of co-operation. He and his older brother have left to the company a rich heritage in their practical exemplification of loyalty and tolerance and good will.

The Saturday half holiday, granted in June, 1881, by the Air Brake Company, appears to have initiated a new practice among large industries. It had an interesting origin. When young George was working in his father's shop at Schenectady, he resented the stern discipline of those days which kept him from playing ball with the other boys. He is reported to have said to his father, "If ever I become an employer, I'll give everybody Saturday afternoon for a holiday." The ideals of the boy became the policies of the man.

The following reported utterance of Samuel Gompers, founder and first president of the American Federation of Labor, after an intense but unsuccessful effort to unionize the Westinghouse Electric & Manufacturing Company, is perhaps the most significant as it is the most notable tribute to the Westinghouse spirit.

"I will say this for George Westinghouse. If all employers of men treated their employees with the same consideration he does, the American Federation of Labor would have to go out of existence."

What was the dominating purpose of Westinghouse? It was not to get money, except as a means for extending his activities. Usually reticent, he once told a personal friend of his supreme desire "to do something which would contribute to human comfort and human happiness." When we contemplate the new industries he created, with their opportunities for useful employment in producing new products which continue to contribute to human comfort and happiness, we see that few men have so fully realized their chief ambition in life as did George Westinghouse.

# EPILOGUE

C. F. Scott: Mr. Chairman, in your opening sketch of Westinghouse, you said that he made the work of Watt and Stephenson and Faraday vastly more effective. Our reminiscences show concretely how he did it, how he amplified the usefulness of power and transportation and electricity, three great agencies of applied science in the progress of civilization. We have traced great achievements from simple ideas in his habitual quest for a better way to do things. His magic wand was persistent effort; urged to take a vacation for pleasure, he replied, "Work is my pleasure."

A gift for quick concentration and an unusual memory enabled him to shift rapidly from one of his many activities to another. Some ideas matured quickly; some major projects required a decade; others, several.

Colonel Prout, in "A Life of Westinghouse," indicates his preeminent traits as imagination, fortitude, serene courage in adversity, audacity, persistence, concentration, memory, association, resourcefulness, complete self-reliance; a good deal more than a genius, he was a man of balanced character, of high and simple standards, strong and gentle, acute and sincere. These qualities supplemented his heritage of health and intellect and character. Dominated by a dynamic personality and an invincible will, he was an outstanding figure in the Engineering Renaissance which preceded the turn of the century.

In developing new things, his great satisfaction was the creating of new industries giving useful employment to many men. Gaging his success in dollars, the pay rolls of his companies have aggregated billions. And his industries aided others by furnishing machinery and power.

But, in larger terms, his whole career offers a solution to a pressing problem of our new industrial order. He solved technological unemployment by creating new employment, new inventions, new industries. His aim was not the accumulation of riches, but the creation of new wealth.

He was a pioneer leading the way through the perplexities of a confused and changing civilization to the realization of its new possibilities.

# *Evening Addresses*

## GEORGE WESTINGHOUSE, THE MAN
PAUL D. CRAVATH, *Attorney, New York City*


## ACHIEVEMENTS OF WESTINGHOUSE
## AS FACTORS IN OUR MODERN LIFE
JAMES ROWLAND ANGELL, *President of Yale University*

GEORGE WESTINGHOUSE AT WORK.

# GEORGE WESTINGHOUSE
# THE MAN

*By* PAUL D. CRAVATH

I HAVE reached that unfortunate age when frequently recurring semicentennials are a constant reminder that I have been on the stage of life beyond the allotted span of three score years and ten. This year happens to be the fiftieth anniversary of the beginning of my association with George Westinghouse. He was my first important client, and my association with him until a short time before his death was very close and intimate. I confess that on this occasion, when most of you who had no close personal contact with Mr. Westinghouse are thinking of the inventor, it is the man, and not the inventor, that dominates the memories of my long association with him, so that the topic you have assigned to me fits in with my mood.

I first met Mr. Westinghouse in the fall of 1884 when I stopped off at Pittsburgh on the way from my home in the West to begin my training for the bar in a law school in the East. I shall never forget the graciousness with which this busy man interrupted his work to talk with me, a callow youth of whom he had never heard; nor shall I ever forget the impression of simplicity and radiating energy that he made upon me.

Whenever I visit the great works of the Westinghouse Electric & Manufacturing Company at East Pittsburgh, I am reminded of my second meeting with Mr. Westinghouse. It was in the fall of 1886, in the company's little shop, which then occupied one floor of a small building in Pittsburgh. I remember, as vividly as though it were yesterday, the enthusiasm with which he spoke, even to a humble visitor like myself, of the unbounded possibilities of electricity applied to the service of man and, more especially, of the great destiny of the alternating current.

It was soon after that, when Mr. Westinghouse, with characteristic courage and breadth of vision, had chosen the largest city in the country in which to demonstrate the superiority of alternating current for central-station lighting, that he acquired control of the high-tension electric-lighting enterprises in New York which were destined to play so important a part in the development of his plans. It was as counsel for those enterprises that I began my association with Mr. Westinghouse—an association that was destined to become the most absorbing and inspiring relationship of my life. For 25 years my relations with Mr. Westinghouse were most intimate.

During that period, in my humble role, I worked at his side in the development of his electrical enterprises which, after the successful establishment of the Air Brake Company, absorbed the major part of his energy and interest. I saw him thus intimately under almost every conceivable condition—in his home, at his office, in his factory, in his private car which was almost another home, abroad, as well as in this country. I saw him when he was elated by successful achievement, and amid disappointments and discouragement, and more than once in the face of threatening disaster. I saw him when he was carrying a load of responsibility under which any other man whom I have ever known would have fallen. He was always the same; simple, unassuming, direct, frank, courageous, unfaltering in his faith, and supremely confident in the ultimate triumph of his plans. I have seen him wearied almost beyond endurance; disappointed beyond expression over some miscarriage of his plans; wounded in his feelings because he had discovered stupidity where he expected intelligence, discouragement where he had expected encouragement, disloyalty where he had a right to expect loyalty. I have seen him more than once when every man about him despaired of his being able to attain the ends for which he was striving and advised surrender or compromise, but I have never known him to acknowledge defeat nor to yield to discouragement, nor to falter in his efforts to accomplish his main objectives.

Comparing George Westinghouse with the other men of his generation who acquired conspicuous positions in the world of industry and finance, it is my considered judgment that no man I have known combined so many of the qualities that make for greatness. The qualities that constitute genius in a human being defy definition. Judged by the standards that I am able to apply, George Westinghouse was a great genius. I assume that all will agree, indeed, the world recognizes, that he was a genius in the field of invention and mechanics. It would be unbecoming for an ignoramus like me to discuss here this phase of Mr. Westinghouse's genius.

### A GREAT INVENTOR, ORGANIZER, AND FINANCIER

Besides being a great inventor, Mr. Westinghouse was a great organizer. Perhaps in his lifetime this assertion would have been questioned by some. I do not see how it can be questioned now. Remember that I am attributing to him as an organizer the qualities of greatness, and not the quality of superficial efficiency. He undoubtedly had the faults of his qualities. Every great man has. Judged by standards of temporary efficiency and by immediate results, his methods of organization sometimes seemed unsound. They were often irritating to his associates. He was apt to be careless of immediate success and to look far ahead for ultimate results. He had the strength of character and the wisdom to submit to temporary inconvenience and to sacrifice temporary advantage to achieve his ultimate ends. Now that we can begin to look back upon Mr. Westinghouse's achievements as an organizer with some approach to the perspective of the historian, we must agree that as an organizer, Mr. Westinghouse manifested qualities of real greatness. Not always unerring in his choice of men, he was always sound in the selection of the fundamental principles which underlay his method of organization. He was a great personal leader, and inspired devotion and affection among his fellow-workers of all ranks. By his own boundless industry and energy he set an example of vigorous and untiring effort that vitalized all the organizations of which he was the head. Every enterprise that he created was built on foundations that were essentially sound and strong. Those foundations have proved able to carry the enormous structures that only his vision was able to foresee.

It is a sad commentary on the limitations of human wisdom that the full fruition of Mr. Westinghouse's plans as an organizer came only after his death. The great enterprises that he founded, some still bearing his name, others transferred to different affiliations, are today achieving signal success along the lines that he laid down, and in the main by men developed under the inspiration of his leadership. He was the soul of the enterprises that he created. That soul is immortal.

BIRTHPLACE OF GEORGE WESTINGHOUSE.

THE PARENTS OF GEORGE WESTINGHOUSE.

It still goes marching on, and will forever animate the enterprises upon which almost a half million people depend for their livelihood —enterprises that are all devoted to increasing the comfort, safety, and happiness of the world. Has any organizer of our day left a comparable record? Is there any other for whom posterity can make so convincing a claim for qualities of true greatness?

Besides being a great inventor and a great organizer, Mr. Westinghouse was, in my estimation, a great financier. This claim would have been questioned by many during his lifetime—some would doubtless question it now. I prophesy it will not be questioned by posterity. I don't say that he was a prudent financier, especially if judged by the standards of Wall Street or of orthodox banking circles in Pittsburgh, but I do claim that he was a great financier. If he had been what we are pleased to call a prudent financier he probably would not have been a great one.

Let us analyze Mr. Westinghouse's claim to greatness as a financier. He was a pioneer in at least four important fields of industry. His enterprises from their very nature required enormous capital. Several, indeed all, of his enterprises were of such character that long periods of experiment and development necessarily preceded the ultimate success that would yield profits. Capital for enterprises of that character, which could not show an earning statement, was difficult to obtain, and yet Mr. Westinghouse, starting life without capital of his own, was able to obtain almost unaided, by the sheer force of his faith, by his power to inspire confidence, by the qualities of his genius, the enormous sums required for the development of his enterprises. He rarely numbered among his close associates important financiers or wealthy men. This may have been a fault, but it was a limitation growing out of the very qualities of his genius. He found it difficult to work with so-called financiers. What seemed to him to be their lack of vision and faith was always annoying to him. While he often tried to work in concert with strong financial associates, he usually found himself in periods of financial stress, compelled to rely upon his own energy and his own resourcefulness. In at least two great financial crises, when the financiers had given up the task as hopeless, Mr. Westinghouse, by his faith, by his untiring energy, and by the exercise of a power to influence men that I have never seen equaled, was able to weather the financial storm, raise enormous sums of money, and restore his enterprises to a sound financial position when his critics and most of his friends were certain that he was facing a crushing defeat.

It was inevitable that a man of George Westinghouse's courage and boldness should suffer financial setbacks; but he never suffered financial defeat. Today all the enterprises that he founded are sound and prosperous. Their financial structures are of his building. Those structures rest upon the sound foundations that he laid. These enterprises, employing, as they do, not far from a quarter of a billion dollars of capital, were financed by Mr. Westinghouse almost unaided and often in the face of discouragement and opposition. They constitute the monument to his success as a financier. I say, therefore, that he was a great financier, and I prophesy that that will be the verdict of history.

In all these fields of endeavor—as an inventor, as an organizer, and as a financier—judged by the standards that I am able to apply, I think he was a great genius. In each field he combined, beyond any man I have ever known, the qualities that seem to me to go to make up genius. They are mental energy, imagination, faith, courage, and character. These qualities were combined in George Westinghouse to a remarkable degree. Any man who has been his business associate for a quarter of a century has often seen him under circumstances that required the exercise of all these qualities. A man who lacked any of them could not have carried the burden in the face of discouragement and opposition that so often rested upon his shoulders.

### IMAGINATION, FAITH, AND COURAGE MADE HIM A GENIUS

The qualities of George Westinghouse which, it seems to me, gave him the supreme quality of genius, were the qualities of imagination, faith, and courage. We know many men of great mental vigor; we know many men of strong character. Those qualities are, of course, the background of any successful career, but I am sure none of us has ever known a man who combined the qualities of faith, imagination, and courage as they were combined in George Westinghouse. Those who are familiar with his enterprises are constantly finding new evidence of these qualities. A very interesting—almost dramatic —instance came to my attention in London during the last year of the War. I presume that most of Mr. Westinghouse's associates would look upon the British Westinghouse Electric Company as one of his failures. In one sense it was a failure, yet the conception out of which that enterprise grew was the conception of a great man, whose vision, imagination, and courage carried him beyond the limits of prudence and business discretion.

During the European War, one of the strongest groups of business minds in Great Britain determined to enter the electrical field. They purchased the British Westinghouse Electric Company. One of these men asked me to spend an evening with him and a few of his associates to give them such information as I could about the early history of the enterprise. Their leader asked me to explain to them the reasons that prompted Mr. Westinghouse to organize the British Westinghouse Electric Company and build the immense works at Manchester, which, until the outbreak of the War, were much larger than the business which the company had been able to secure would justify. I tried to give Mr. Westinghouse's conceptions as I remembered them; that the high-tension alternating current was sure to become the foundation of all central-station development; that England was an ideal field for the extensive use and distribution of electricity; that most of the British railroads had such a dense traffic as to be practically suburban roads, according to American standards; that the most economical method of providing electrical power for the United Kingdom was by the establishment of generating stations near the coal mines so that instead of distributing coal, electricity would be distributed; that instead of many central stations scattered all over the country there should be a few at strategic locations; that as the financial structure of the railroad enterprises of Great Britain was such that they would find it difficult to raise new capital, there should be separate organizations separately financed, for developing the electrical power and selling it to the railroads. When I had finished my story, the leader of the group turned to his associates and said with real emotion: "This is most remarkable. The vision of Mr. Westinghouse is almost word for word our vision. The plans he formed are almost identical with the plans we propose to carry through." Then he turned to me and said: "Mr. Westinghouse's conception of what should be done was faultless. It was his misfortune that he underestimated the force of British conservatism, and was a quarter of a century ahead of the times. If Great Britain had accepted his advice, waste totaling countless millions would have been prevented. It will now be necessary to scrap enormous investments in uneconomical plants to make way for the carrying out of Mr. Westinghouse's plan." He added that so conservative, so slow to adopt new ideas are the

British people that even today the Government would be compelled to apply the spur of legislation to force the adoption of the measures which were proposed by Mr. Westinghouse a quarter of a century earlier. When he finished, I said: "You must agree, gentlemen, that while Mr. Westinghouse may not always have been a prudent man, he was a great man." "Yes," said their leader, "Mr. Westinghouse was a great man."

In what I have said I have dwelt, as it is proper that I should dwell, upon Mr. Westinghouse's qualities of greatness, for his former associates are anxious that the world should recognize, as it surely will, those qualities in the man who for so many years we were proud to call our chief; but I am sure that those of you who were his co-workers, will find yourselves tonight thinking not of the man of genius, but of the simple, unaffected, loyal friend whom we affectionately called, "The Old Man;" who was never too deeply absorbed to say a word of kindness and encouragement to an associate or subordinate; never so engrossed in his great achievements that he did not have time to help a friend who needed his help. It would seem profanation if I attempted by any words of mine to add to the brightness of the image that memory has implanted in our hearts. After all, was it not the finest thing about Mr. Westinghouse, man of genius as he was, that he retained from the beginning to the end of his career of great achievement, that simplicity and genuineness of character that endeared him to all his associates? I need not say to them that we shall never see his like again.

CENTRAL PANEL, THE GEORGE WESTINGHOUSE MEMORIAL

"This memorial, unveiled October 6, 1930, in honor of George Westinghouse, is an enduring testimonial to the esteem, affection and loyalty of sixty thousand employees of the great industrial organizations of which he was the founder. In his later years rightly called 'the greatest living engineer,' George Westinghouse accomplished much of first importance to mankind through his ingenuity, persistence, courage, integrity and leadership. By the invention of the air brake and of automatic signaling devices, he led the world in the development of appliances for the promotion of speed, safety and economy of transportation. By his early vision of the value of the alternating current electric system he brought about a revolution in the transmission of electric power. His achievements were great, his energy and enthusiasm boundless, and his character beyond reproach; a shining mark for the encouragement of American youth."

*Westinghouse Memorial Association Trustees:*
A. L. Humphrey, A. W. Robertson, E. M. Herr, F. A. Merrick, John F. Miller.

61

LEFT WING, THE GEORGE WESTINGHOUSE MEMORIAL

*Left Panel*—Railway Electrification
"The first substitution of high voltage electricity for operating a main line railroad."

*Center Panel*—Steam-Electric Power
"Steam turbines by vast power in small space and great economy have become a basic source of universal electricity."

*Right Panel*—Hydro-Electric Power
"Niagara whose energy converted to electricity served the first great power system and created an industrial empire."

RIGHT WING, THE GEORGE WESTINGHOUSE MEMORIAL

*Left Panel*—Chicago World's Fair
   "Chicago Exposition, 1893, where was first exhibited in operation a complete alternating system of power distribution."

*Center Panel*—The Air Brake
   "The Westinghouse Air Brake immeasurably increased the speed safety and economy of railway transportation throughout the world."

*Right Panel*—Automatic Signaling Devices
   "Modern signaling systems which enable speed with safety in transportation are the results of the vision of Westinghouse."

FIGURE REPRESENTING AMERICAN YOUTH, FACING CENTRAL
PANEL OF THE GEORGE WESTINGHOUSE MEMORIAL.

# ACHIEVEMENTS OF WESTINGHOUSE AS FACTORS IN OUR MODERN LIFE

*By* JAMES ROWLAND ANGELL

IT IS WITH no little hesitation that I have accepted the invitation to speak tonight concerning the distinguished man whose ninetieth birthday is here being honored. I never had the pleasure of meeting him and I am not myself an engineer. These circumstances constitute no small handicap in the effort to deal intelligently and justly with the subject upon which I have been asked to speak.

My disposition to accept the invitation has been stimulated in part by my intimate acquaintance with not a few of the leading men upon whom Mr. Westinghouse leaned at one time and another in the development of his great enterprises, and in part by reason of the fact that the thoughtful layman finds himself so completely immersed in a civilization which owes much to men like Mr. Westinghouse that on occasion his voice may properly be heard when efforts are made to evaluate the implications of engineering achievements upon the flow of human history.

The career of Mr. Westinghouse has more than once been dealt with by persons who knew him intimately and watched his development from a simple country boy to one of the great leaders in the industrial world. The portraits which have thus been drawn all agree in setting forth a man of robust integrity of character, of great essential modesty, and of extraordinary powers of unremitting toil. It does not appear that in his boyhood he gave any evidences of intellectual brilliancy. One rather gathers that such qualities were entirely missing, but that from early childhood on he disclosed the inclination to devote his entire time and energy to problems which interested him and only to such, most of them evidently being of a mechanical nature. Certainly it seems to be clear that throughout his life his outstanding successes were the results of indomitable energy, of incessant labor, and complete inability ever to be discouraged. He seems also to have disclosed rather early in his career the qualities so essential in the promotion of new ideas in the commercial and industrial world, to wit, the power to intrigue influential men with his plans and to persuade them to take up with his ideas. The one outstanding failure in this respect was perhaps his inability ever to induce his own father to give much support to his early ventures. This is probably one of the many conspicuous instances in history of the prophet being without honor in his own country. Furthermore, it is always difficult for parents to take quite seriously revolutionary ideas proposed by their children.

## MAJOR ACHIEVEMENTS

Those who are best fitted to judge seem to agree fairly well on the half dozen outstanding accomplishments by which Mr. Westinghouse is likely to be longest remembered. So far as concerns the general public, the invention and perfection of the air brake easily stands first, and this despite the fact that he had been preceded in his idea of using air for this purpose by at least one other inventor, to whom, however, he owed nothing whatever, so far as is known. If his biographers are correct, Mr. Westinghouse himself was disposed to agree with certain authorities in the railroad world that his invention of the friction draft gear, applicable to the speed control of railway cars, was of even greater importance. Certainly the device was extremely ingenious and without it the great trains which we use on our American railroads could not be operated with safety. But the same thing is, of course, equally true of the air brake. To this same portion of his contributions to rail transportation belong his inventions of devices for power signaling and for interlocking switches. No modern rail system could possibly operate without these indispensable aids to safety, speed, and convenience.

His early interest in the rotary engine, issuing finally in his epoch-making development and introduction of the steam turbine, must rank high in any list of his achievements. Similarly his championship of the use of the alternating current, with its extraordinary advantages for long-distance transmission, together with the development of the induction motor and of apparatus which enabled alternating current to be converted into direct current, where that form of electrical energy is preferable, so critical for both the financial and the engineering success of the Westinghouse program, marks one of the outstanding accomplishments of engineering progress in the last century. And these things were done in the face of the most powerful and bitter opposition.

While Mr. Westinghouse has not, in the public eye, been so intimately connected with the development of the gas engine as with some of these other successes already mentioned, this was early a subject engaging his active and long-continued interest and his contributions are deeply imbedded in the industrial developments which grew up around this form of prime mover. Intimately connected with this achievement, and in part responsible for his continued sense of its importance, was his development of the use of natural gas and his inventions for its safe transfer and consumption. The list of the patents which were issued to him in the course of his long life covers an amazing variety of ingenious devices, not a few of which have had important industrial and commercial consequences, but those which I have specifically mentioned are, I think, the ones that by common consent are the most likely to carry his name down to posterity in the history of industrial evolution.

### TRANSPORTATION OF PEOPLE, FREIGHT, AND POWER

While their implications extend quite beyond this zone, it is clear that Mr. Westinghouse's interests were first directed to problems of transportation, whether of people, or freight, or power, and that throughout his life all of his important accomplishments, practically without exception, had direct, or indirect, relation to issues of that character. It is perhaps simply an indication of the close dependence of all parts of our mechanical age, one upon another, that, starting with this initial concern for transportation, he should have devised techniques which are significant far beyond the boundaries of their original purposes.

While I find the biographers of Mr. Westinghouse not wholly revealing on this matter, it seems to be clear that he was always highly

ILLUMINATION OF THE CHICAGO WORLD'S FAIR, 1893—ONE OF THE DRAMATIC ACHIEVEMENTS OF GEORGE WESTINGHOUSE'S CAREER.

sensitive to the welfare of his own employees and temperamentally therefore disposed to be sensitive to the needs of the laboring population as a whole. On the other hand, he was obdurate in maintaining an open shop. He exhibited no animosity to unions or union men, when they did not try to exercise coercion, but the nonunion man who did his work efficiently stood on exactly the same level as his union neighbor. In any event, nothing is more certain than that the trend in the modern world, rather definitely confirmed in our own country by the last election, is to regard all these important effects of commercial and industrial methods on large groups of our human brothers as properly and inevitably subject to general social and political consideration.

### CONTEMPORARY FIELDS

Two or three of the most important contemporary fields in which the engineer has been altering the contours of our national life were left largely untouched by Mr. Westinghouse. In two of the instances this perhaps has its explanation in the relative lateness of the pertinent discoveries. Whatever the reasons, it seems in general to be true that he did not actively interest himself in the problems of telegraphy, although he did make an interesting mechanical proposal in connection with the telephone. It happens that the first commercial telephone exchange was opened in New Haven in 1879, and in the same year Westinghouse patented a scheme with auxiliary exchanges which were automatic, and he indicated in detail the specifications for their construction. This shows his interest and understanding in a new art, and his proposal dimly forecast modern machine switching. Nor do we find that the radio or the airplane were in the focus of his immediate concern, nor photography and its most influential form, the cinema. It might, perhaps, have been unfortunate had these vigorously attracted his attention, for the range and variety of his undertakings were such that any large additional exploratory enterprise would have been a source of possible weakness in his organizations—to say nothing of the diversion of his own intelligence from the completely absorbing problems to which he had given his life. Nevertheless, it seems rather improbable that had certain of these developments come at a more favorable period, he would not have followed his usual practice of acquiring important patents and thereupon proceeded to develop them into the most useful possible forms. Certainly nothing is more striking in Mr. Westinghouse's career than the promptness with which he spotted significant inventions of other men and sought to bring them into the area of his own activity. I have yet to encounter a case in which it appears that he, unlike not a few of the conspicuous exploiters of other men's ideas, dealt otherwise than justly, and indeed generously, with the inventors and owners of patented devices. Moreover, it may be that his deep-seated wish to be a pioneer prevented his taking up with some of these forms of inventive ingenuity, because he felt that they were already far on the way to firm establishment before he came into touch with them. In any event, in our general evaluation of Mr. Westinghouse's achievements, it is essential to recognize that to three great technological activities of our time, which seem to be most instantly affecting the patterns of life, to wit, the moving pictures, the airplane (and one may add the lighter-than-air ships), and the radio, he was in no sense a contributor.

### CIVILIZATION FOLLOWS THE ENGINEER

It is in our day and generation essentially a truism that civilization is at many of its most critical points dependent upon the accomplishments of the engineer and that the character of our culture has been repeatedly changing during the last century or two as a result of the impact of mechanical inventions upon the patterns of daily life. This impact extends not only to our dependence in matters of food, clothing, shelter, and travel upon engineering devices, but it has also entered to color the whole character of our economic, commercial, and industrial outlook. To call ours a mercantile or commercial culture is often felt to cast upon it a shadow, but whether it be thought to be an unworthy shadow or not, such a characterization is in most respects transparently correct. The inventions of pure scientists and the applications made of them by inventors and industrial engineers have fundamentally changed the fabric of human life in all but the most completely uncivilized hinterland, and, were these achievements to be suddenly blotted out, our civilization as we now have it would collapse like a pack of cards. The most casual survey of any of a great group of obvious facts exhibits the truth of this assertion. Suppose, for example, that all the processes of refrigeration were unexpectedly destroyed—the modern city would starve in a few days. Take away the devices for the mechanical supply of light and heat and these same cities would be plunged into darkness at night and would be reduced to intolerable suffering through the winter months. Take away the methods of rapid, large-scale transportation, and adequate supplies of food and clothing, and warmth would be quickly menaced. Blot out the radio, the telegraph and telephone, and modern methods of business would be ruinously disorganized. One need not further pursue the parable, although only the most conspicuous examples have been cited of our dependence upon engineering skill, and, if hygiene and physical health were further brought into the picture, the devastating consequences of the removal of these innumerable scientific devices which make for our comfort and protection would be instantly and completely in evidence.

It would be impossible to analyze from the total complex of human effects produced by technical causes just those for which any one man like George Westinghouse is responsible. Indeed, it is only less impossible to determine just what changes in our patterns of human behavior are attributable to particular technological developments to which many individuals may have contributed. What we can in some degree do is to evaluate, roughly, the consequences for civilization and for human welfare and happiness of definite types of engineering achievement. Even this is a precarious undertaking.

### TRANSPORTATION AND NATIONAL DEVELOPMENT

In our own country, with its vast area and its divergent natural resources, even the most phlegmatic imagination can picture something of what rapid transportation of freight and passengers has accomplished. Together with other similar agencies, it has gone far to fuse into one economic nation a great group of territorial empires. California and Florida, 3000 miles apart, furnish New York and Duluth with fresh fruits throughout the winter and fresh vegetables for almost any season. This achievement is partly due to skillful processes of refrigeration, but largely to fast freight, now carried by rail and perhaps presently to be carried still more quickly by air. Without the engineer, none of these things could have been done and we should still be living like our grandfathers, chiefly upon the foodstuffs supplied by the immediate countryside about our homes. What is true of fruits and vegetables is equally true of grains, meats, and fish. Climate and seasons and limitations of soil have been practically wiped out by putting at human disposal the products of the most remote lands. Apart from the sheer aesthetic satisfactions of such a situation for its

REAR ADMIRAL GEORGE W. MELVILLE, U. S. N., GEORGE WESTINGHOUSE,
AND JOHN H. MACALPINE, WHO COLLABORATED IN APPLYING
STEAM TURBINES TO MARINE SERVICE.

beneficiaries, there can be no doubt that diet can thus be made more varied and nutritionally more adequate—certainly far more palatable.

Improved travel and transportation have also revolutionized business methods. The buyer now visits the great centers two or three times a year, whether in his own country or abroad, and determines what to stock and arranges the prices which he is willing to pay, where a generation ago the local middleman and merchant took what the distant manufacturer offered and the local trade had only the choice to take it or leave it. The result of this fundamental alteration in commercial methods, deriving distinctly from improved and cheapened travel, has been not only a vast stimulation of retail business of every kind, but also a tendency to put every part of the world in touch with the developments going on elsewhere. Whether the general uniformizing of tastes and fashions, thus occasioned, is an unmitigated blessing may well be questioned, but of the actual economic and social effects there can be no doubt.

Tourist travel has, as is well understood, become one of the highly important elements in international relations, especially those of a financial character. So far as the individual is concerned, modern transportation has thus opened up an entirely new world of experience. What use the citizen makes of this opportunity depends, of course, upon his intelligence, his imagination, and his general social background. The gross effect of these modern devices for quick and inexpensive movement by land, water, and air is that the world has shrunk to a mere fraction of the dimensions which our colonial ancestors knew. To go from New York to Bombay is far less of a venture and vastly less time-consuming than was the journey, in 1776, from New York to Lake Superior.

### ELECTRIC POWER

Few contributions of the engineer have exercised more far-reaching consequences than the cheap long-distance transportation of power. Industrial plants have sprung up far from water powers and in places where land values were low and the conditions of life for employees simple, inexpensive, and wholesome. Costly power-producing plants have been scrapped and in their places power transmission from a distance has been installed. Such transmission of electricity to run our railroads, trolleys, and subways has long been a familiar element in our lives.

The farmer has similarly had cheap power brought to him to run the various pieces of machinery which the modern farm requires. Needless to say, he has long had electric light.

The changes which for the greater part have been directly due to easy and rapid transport are paralleled in other aspects of life, affected by other engineering achievements. It is thus a commonplace of comment that in earlier days our textiles were made in or near the home. Now we may at any time find ourselves wearing materials fabricated a thousand miles or more away at an amazingly low price, and these are offered to us in a bewildering array of fashions.

Our great-grandfathers read by candlelight, or by poor lamps. We press a button and the whole house is flooded with light. In winter they sat about defective stoves, or huddled over open fires which, with all their aesthetic charm, are poor means for heating a house in our severe climate. We start the thermostatically controlled furnace in the autumn and forget it until spring once more ushers in the summer, and, while no such devices are foolproof and none can be counted on to work wholly without occasional interruption, they are extremely effective in preserving appropriate temperatures and in ridding the housekeeper of the endless routine of replenishing fires and caring for ashes. Westinghouse first solved this problem for the denizens of favored regions by devising means for the distribution of natural gas. Coupled with modern methods of heating may well be mentioned ventilating systems and air cooling, for all of which we are beholden to the engineer. And for most of these as well as for our refrigerators and for a score of other appliances in the modern home we are dependent upon electric power which comes to us by the system which Westinghouse so successfully sponsored.

### ENGINEERING ACHIEVEMENT AND ECONOMIC ADJUSTMENT

I have said nothing of the crucial achievements connected with the control of water supplies, the disposition of sewage, and the surveillance of disease-free milk and foods, all of which are blessings that we owe in part to engineers and in part to our medical scientists. The dividing line between the scientist, in whatever field he may be proficient, and the engineer who makes his discoveries available to men by practical devices, is always difficult to draw. For our present purposes, it is not essential that we should make this effort. Suffice it to say that, together with the dramatic changes which we have touched

upon in the form and manner of modern life, due to the contributions
of engineers, these which are related directly to health are of the very
first consequence. Let me repeat that it is quite impossible to sort
out just those changes in our culture and civilization for which Mr.
Westinghouse is most immediately responsible; but it is an entirely
safe assertion that in transportation broadly conceived lay his greatest contribution and that the social and economic changes deriving
most immediately thence are those for which we are chiefly indebted
to him—and a tremendous debt it is.

A few years ago our newspapers and periodicals were much concerned with an intellectual fad calling itself technocracy. This has
largely passed out of the area of acute interest, but it did raise certain
enduring questions which cannot, and must not, be forgotten. For
one of the conspicuous facts about mechanical inventions is that when
they affect industrial activities giving employment to large groups of
people, they may occasion sudden large-scale dislocations of labor
with periods of unemployment, which compel society to step in and,
in one form or another, assist in the economic readjustment. This is
nothing new in the world. It has been true ever since the beginning
of the great industrial movement in Britain in the early part of the
last century. It is important in the present context of which I am
speaking simply because it is one of the most striking demonstrations
of the effect which engineering progress may have upon the social and
economic life of a nation. The time has long passed when we can look
upon these developments as simply interesting eccentricities exercis-
ing purely local effects. They constitute part and parcel of the very
fiber of our contemporary life and when we are willing to accept the
benefits which they bring to us in the form of cheaper and better food
and raiment and such like blessings, we must be willing to see to it
that, by whatever precautions, our neighbors are not compelled to pay
in poverty and suffering for the advantages which we enjoy. Nor can
we wish off on the individual industrialist, or manufacturer, the entire responsibility for this situation. So long as we issue patents and
protect the holders and permit them to manufacture their laborsaving devices and the goods flow from them, we are morally bound to
see to it that all parts of the community are protected, as well as the
patentee, from any ill-advised consequences which may flow from his
industry and intelligence. The fact that in the long run laborsaving
devices apparently lead to the discovery and perfection of new modes

WESTINGHOUSE MEMORIAL BRIDGE, LINCOLN HIGHWAY, EAST PITTSBURGH, PA., WITH PLANT OF THE WESTINGHOUSE ELECTRIC & MANUFACTURING COMPANY IN BACKGROUND.

of human activity, which ultimately engage the displaced labor population, does not exonerate us from a due regard to the consequences during the periods of transition when fresh equilibrium is being established.

Practically all of the changes which during the last century have determined the external complexion of civilization, and much of its internal quality, rest on just such ingenious and carefully matured devices as George Westinghouse gave his life to perfecting, and the great enterprises of industry and commerce and transportation constantly testify to the profound effect it has all had upon the daily experience of millions of people. Moreover, there can be no question that through these agencies the world has been brought into a more closely knit relationship of mutual dependence and that in many respects the life of the average person has been made safer, easier, and more enjoyable. Nevertheless, there are those who insist upon raising the question whether in its fundamental essentials human life has been really enriched by all these changes, for which we are indebted to the technological developments of the last century or two. Such persons insist on asking whether we are really happier for it all, whether we are really more civilized. Is our culture richer, more fruitful, more potent for future progress, than it was before these things occurred? Is human life better safeguarded? Is poverty less a menace, are crime and disease less sinister in their consequences? To some of these questions an unequivocal affirmative can surely be given.

### HUMAN WELFARE VS. SHEER DESTRUCTION

Human health is certainly better protected, and disease, particularly epidemic disease, is, in large measure, on the way to be scotched. But, if one be committed to an austere and stoic philosophy of life, one may with some show of cogency, defend the simpler, more independent and more rigorous manner of living, in which luxury was relatively infrequent and comfort far less familiar than today. Men who entertain that view are likely to assert that the essential moral quality of human character has been weakened and that not a few of the by-products of scientific and technological discovery have been vulgarizing to taste and disintegrating to morals. They raise the question whether mankind has as yet achieved a mentality and a moral fiber to make all these great contributions to progress really significant and valuable. They are likely to urge that such changes have come too fast and that we really now need a prolonged moratorium in the field of scientific and engineering invention in order that we may socially and spiritually catch up to the physical factors of the world in which we live.

Questions of this kind are in a sense perhaps romantic, for, after all, the changes are here and society is in process of adjusting itself to them. Nevertheless, it is a fact that the same scientific and engineering skill which, turned in one direction, produces human happiness and welfare may, with little or no change except that of the moral purpose of the user, be converted into means for sheer destruction. The familiar illustration of all this is the direction of the skill of the chemist away from useful employments which promote health and happiness to the production of poison gases by which millions of innocent people may in an instant be put to death. This extreme illustration can be easily capped by dozens of others in which direct physical injury to human life is decreasingly in evidence, but where the disintegrating effects upon morals may be convincingly exhibited.

All this line of consideration reduces to the familiar ethical truism that no fact taken of and by itself is necessarily either good or evil, but inevitably depends upon the purpose to which it is put and the results which emanate from its use. In this sense, I think it must be admitted that the great task of our day and generation lies more in the field of morals and even religion, if you will, than in the field of engineering and economics narrowly conceived. As I read the life of George Westinghouse, I carry away the conviction that he would himself be increasingly disposed to take this view had his life rounded out the century. Certainly his own career is a vivid object lesson in the advantages of simple living, high aims, and hard work, and it is impossible to believe that he would have felt anything but regret could it be shown that the industrial age to which he gave such brilliant leadership throughout his life was contributing to soften the fiber of the race, or to introduce into it elements of moral disintegration. Most of us believe that this is quite untrue and that the great engineering victories of men like Westinghouse constitute a blazing challenge to us to build a social order which is able to incorporate in itself all these blessings, while safeguarding the finest values that inhere in the human spirit.

PRINTED IN U.S.A.
THE EDDY PRESS CORPORATI
PITTSBURGH, PA.